The little leaf
and
The loose tooth

M
Macmillan Education

The little leaf

A tree stood in the garden.

The wind began to blow.

A little leaf fell off the tree.

It fell down and down and down.

It landed on the grass under the tree.

A cat was sitting on the grass.

Hello little green leaf, said the cat.

Can I play with you?

The little leaf was about to say yes,
when the wind began to blow again.
Whoosh! went the wind and
it lifted the little leaf
up and up into the sky.
The wind took it a long way.
Then it dropped the little leaf gently
at the side of a road.

Hello little yellow leaf, said a bird
by the side of the road.
Are you going to stay with me?
That's funny, said the little leaf.
The cat said I was green.
Now the bird says I am yellow.
I wonder what colour I am?

The leaf was just about to ask the bird
when the wind began to blow again.
Whoosh! went the wind and it lifted
the little leaf up and up into the sky.
The wind took it a long way.
Then it dropped the little leaf gently
in a big field.

There was a big animal in the field.
The big animal came over to look at
the little leaf.
Moo, said the animal.
Hello little orange leaf.
That's funny, said the little leaf.
The cat said I was green and
the bird said I was yellow.
Now the cow says I am orange.
I wonder what colour I am?

The little leaf was just about
to ask the cow when the wind began
to blow again.
Whoosh! went the wind and it lifted
the little leaf up and up into the sky.
The wind took it a long way.
Then it dropped the little leaf gently
on the top of a big hill.

The little leaf lay there for some time.
Then a goat came up to it.
Hello little red leaf, said the goat.
Have you come to live
on the hill with me?
That's funny, said the little leaf.
The cat said I was green and
the bird said I was yellow and
the cow said I was orange.
Now the goat says I am red.
I wonder what colour I am?

The little leaf was just about to ask
the goat when the wind began
to blow again.
Whoosh! went the wind and it lifted
the little leaf up and up into the sky.
The wind took it a long way.
Then it dropped the little leaf gently
in a farm.

The little leaf lay quite still.
Hello little brown leaf, said a pig.
I nearly ate you just now.
Did the wind bring you here?
That's funny, said the little leaf.
The cat said I was green and
the bird said I was yellow and
the cow said I was orange and
the goat said I was red.
Now the pig says I am brown.
I wonder what colour I am?

Just then a little boy saw
the little leaf.
He picked it up.
Look, he said to his mother.
Look at this little gold leaf.
And look at all the other leaves.
They are green and yellow and orange and
red and brown and gold.
Yes, said his mother.
Now that summer is over, the leaves
are the colours of autumn.

The loose tooth

It was nearly time for school but
Sita was late.
I can't eat my breakfast, she said.
My loose tooth hurts.
Let me pull it out, said Mum.
No thank you, said Sita.
Well you get it out, said Mum.
Bring it home and I'll give you
some money for it.

Sita put on her jacket and
her new yellow boots.
The door bell rang.
That's Nick, said Sita.
I'm going now. Goodbye Mum.
Nick and Sita went down the path.
Would you like a toffee? said Nick.
Yes please, said Sita.

Nick and Sita walked side by side
and kicked up the leaves.
Swish, swish! Swish, swish!
Then Sita said, There's something
in my toffee Nick.
Oh look. It's my tooth.
It's come out.
I'll put it in my hankie.
When I get home, Mum will give me
some money for it.

Sita put her tooth in her hankie and
she put the hankie in her pocket.
Then she and Nick walked on again
through the leaves. Swish, swish!
But just then Sita began to . . .
began to . . . began to . . . sneeze.
Three big sneezes.

Near school, they met Su.
My tooth has come out Su, said Sita.
I've put it in my hankie and
when I get home, Mum will
give me some money.
Let me see it, said Su.
Sita pulled out her hankie.
Oh dear, she said. Where is my tooth?
I've lost it!
We'll help you look for it,
said both her friends.

There it is, said Nick but
it was only a bit of paper.
What have you lost? said a lady.
So they told her about the tooth.
If Sita doesn't find it, said Su,
she won't get any money.
I'll help you look, said the lady.
So they all looked for the tooth.

There it is, said Su but
it was only a bit of rag.
What have you lost?
said a boy with a dog.
So they told him about the tooth.
If Sita doesn't find it, said Nick,
she won't get any money.
I'll help you look,
said the boy with the dog.
So they all looked for the tooth.

A road man was coming to
sweep up the leaves.
Wait, wait, cried Sita.
I've lost my tooth in the leaves.
What good is it now? said the road man.
You can't eat with it any more!
Yes, but Mum will give me
some money for it, said Sita.
The road man said she would never find
a little tooth in all the leaves but
he helped them all look.

19

Just then Miss Peck began
to ring the school bell.
She saw Sita and Nick and Su and
the lady and the boy with the dog
and the road sweeper.
What are you doing? said Miss Peck.
I've lost my tooth, said Sita.
We are helping her look for it,
said all the others.

Well now it is time for school,
said Miss Peck. You won't find it now.
And I won't get any money from
my Mum, Sita said sadly.
She began to walk into the playground.
Ow! My foot hurts now, she said.
There's something in my boot.

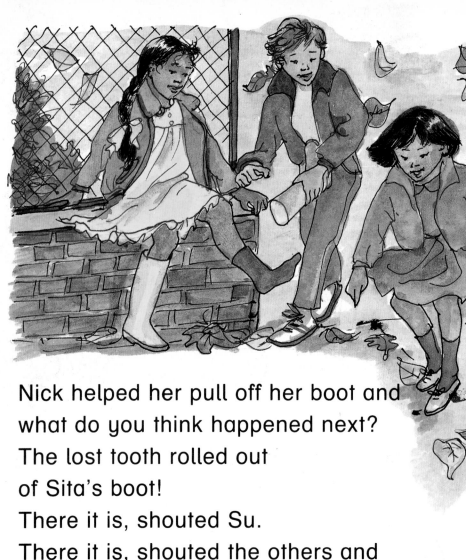

Nick helped her pull off her boot and
what do you think happened next?
The lost tooth rolled out
of Sita's boot!
There it is, shouted Su.
There it is, shouted the others and
they all began to laugh.
Now you will get your money after all,
they all said.

Sita thanked them all, then
the lady went off to do her shopping,
the boy went off to
take the dog for a walk,
the road man went off to
sweep up the leaves and
the children went into school.

When Sita got home after school,
she told her Mum how
she had lost her tooth.
Here it is Mum, said Sita.
And here is your money, said Mum.